W9-BRM-274

ANNE GEDDES

1996
Datebook

A COLLECTION OF IMAGES

ISBN 1-55912-914-X

© Anne Geddes 1994

Published in 1995 by Cedco Publishing Company,
2955 Kerner Blvd, San Rafael, CA 94901.
First USA edition 1995.

Designed by Jane Seabrook
Produced by Kel Geddes
Color separations by Star Graphics
Artwork by Advision
Printed in Hong Kong

ANNE GEDDES

Anne Geddes, an Australian born photographer residing in Auckland, New Zealand, has won the hearts of people internationally with her unique and special images of children.

Her exceptional images have also received resounding critical acclaim, attracting a host of professional awards, including being awarded a prestigious "Fellow of Photography."

Her work now widely recognized and appreciated in America, initially from Greeting Cards and Posters, is now available in Calendars and a range of hard covered Books, including the ever popular Datebook.

Anne's images capture the joy and love to be found in all young children. After all, she says, "To be able to capture on film the innocence, trust and happiness that is inherent in the next generation is a very special responsibility. I would only hope that my images are able to help in a small, yet meaningful way, to protect and nourish what is possibly our greatest natural resource."

Anne is married to her friend and business partner, Kel. Together they have two children.

1996 Calendar

January

S	M	T	W	T	F	S
	1	2	3	4	5	6
7	8	9	10	11	12	13
14	15	16	17	18	19	20
21	22	23	24	25	26	27
28	29	30	31			

February

S	M	T	W	T	F	S
				1	2	3
4	5	6	7	8	9	10
11	12	13	14	15	16	17
18	19	20	21	22	23	24
25	26	27	28	29		

March

S	M	T	W	T	F	S
					1	2
3	4	5	6	7	8	9
10	11	12	13	14	15	16
17	18	19	20	21	22	23
24	25	26	27	28	29	30
31						

April

S	M	T	W	T	F	S
	1	2	3	4	5	6
7	8	9	10	11	12	13
14	15	16	17	18	19	20
21	22	23	24	25	26	27
28	29	30				

May

S	M	T	W	T	F	S
			1	2	3	4
5	6	7	8	9	10	11
12	13	14	15	16	17	18
19	20	21	22	23	24	25
26	27	28	29	30	31	

June

S	M	T	W	T	F	S
						1
2	3	4	5	6	7	8
9	10	11	12	13	14	15
16	17	18	19	20	21	22
23	24	25	26	27	28	29
30						

July

S	M	T	W	T	F	S
	1	2	3	4	5	6
7	8	9	10	11	12	13
14	15	16	17	18	19	20
21	22	23	24	25	26	27
28	29	30	31			

August

S	M	T	W	T	F	S
				1	2	3
4	5	6	7	8	9	10
11	12	13	14	15	16	17
18	19	20	21	22	23	24
25	26	27	28	29	30	31

September

S	M	T	W	T	F	S
1	2	3	4	5	6	7
8	9	10	11	12	13	14
15	16	17	18	19	20	21
22	23	24	25	26	27	28
29	30					

October

S	M	T	W	T	F	S
		1	2	3	4	5
6	7	8	9	10	11	12
13	14	15	16	17	18	19
20	21	22	23	24	25	26
27	28	29	30	31		

November

S	M	T	W	T	F	S
					1	2
3	4	5	6	7	8	9
10	11	12	13	14	15	16
17	18	19	20	21	22	23
24	25	26	27	28	29	30

December

S	M	T	W	T	F	S
1	2	3	4	5	6	7
8	9	10	11	12	13	14
15	16	17	18	19	20	21
22	23	24	25	26	27	28
29	30	31				

DECEMBER · JANUARY

SUNDAY	31
MONDAY *New Year's Day*	1
TUESDAY	2
WEDNESDAY	3
THURSDAY	4
FRIDAY ○ *Full Moon*	5
SATURDAY	6

ANNE GEDDES

JANUARY

SUNDAY   7

MONDAY   8

TUESDAY   9

WEDNESDAY   10

THURSDAY   11

FRIDAY   12

SATURDAY   13

◑
Last Quarter Moon

ANNE GEDDES

JANUARY

SUNDAY	14
MONDAY *Martin Luther King Day*	15
TUESDAY	16
WEDNESDAY	17
THURSDAY	18
FRIDAY	19
SATURDAY	20

●
New Moon

JANUARY

SUNDAY	21
MONDAY	22
TUESDAY	23
WEDNESDAY	24
THURSDAY	25
FRIDAY	26
SATURDAY	27

◑
First Quarter Moon

ANNE GEDDES

JANUARY - FEBRUARY

SUNDAY	28
MONDAY	29
TUESDAY	30
WEDNESDAY	31
THURSDAY	1
FRIDAY	2
SATURDAY	3

FEBRUARY

SUNDAY   4

○
Full Moon

MONDAY   5

TUESDAY   6

WEDNESDAY   7

THURSDAY   8

FRIDAY   9

SATURDAY   10

FEBRUARY

SUNDAY 11

MONDAY 12
Lincoln's Birthday

◑
Last Quarter Moon

TUESDAY 13

WEDNESDAY 14
St. Valentine's Day

THURSDAY 15

FRIDAY 16

SATURDAY 17

FEBRUARY

SUNDAY

18

●
New Moon

MONDAY
Presidents' Day

19

TUESDAY

20

WEDNESDAY
Ash Wednesday

21

THURSDAY
Washington's Birthday

22

FRIDAY

23

SATURDAY

24

FEBRUARY - MARCH

SUNDAY	25
MONDAY	26

◐
First Quarter Moon

TUESDAY	27
WEDNESDAY	28
THURSDAY	29
FRIDAY	1
SATURDAY	2

ANNE GEDDES

MARCH

SUNDAY	3
MONDAY	4
TUESDAY	5

○
Full Moon

WEDNESDAY	6
THURSDAY	7
FRIDAY *International Women's Day*	8
SATURDAY	9

ANNE GEDDES

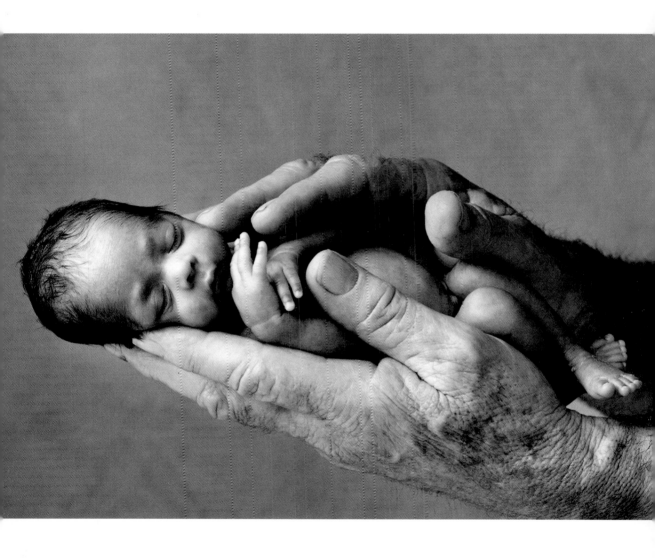

MARCH

SUNDAY	10
MONDAY	11
TUESDAY	12

◗
Last Quarter Moon

WEDNESDAY	13
THURSDAY	14
FRIDAY	15
SATURDAY	16

ANNE GEDDES

MARCH

SUNDAY *St. Patrick's Day*	17
MONDAY	18
TUESDAY	19
● *New Moon*	
WEDNESDAY *Vernal Equinox* *3:04 A.M. E.S.T.*	20
THURSDAY	21
FRIDAY	22
SATURDAY	23

MARCH

SUNDAY	24
MONDAY	25
TUESDAY	26

◐
First Quarter Moon

WEDNESDAY	27
THURSDAY	28
FRIDAY	29
SATURDAY	30

MARCH - APRIL

SUNDAY *Palm Sunday*	31
MONDAY	1
TUESDAY	2
WEDNESDAY *Passover begins (at sunset)* ○ *Full Moon*	3
THURSDAY	4
FRIDAY *Good Friday*	5
SATURDAY	6

ANNE GEDDES

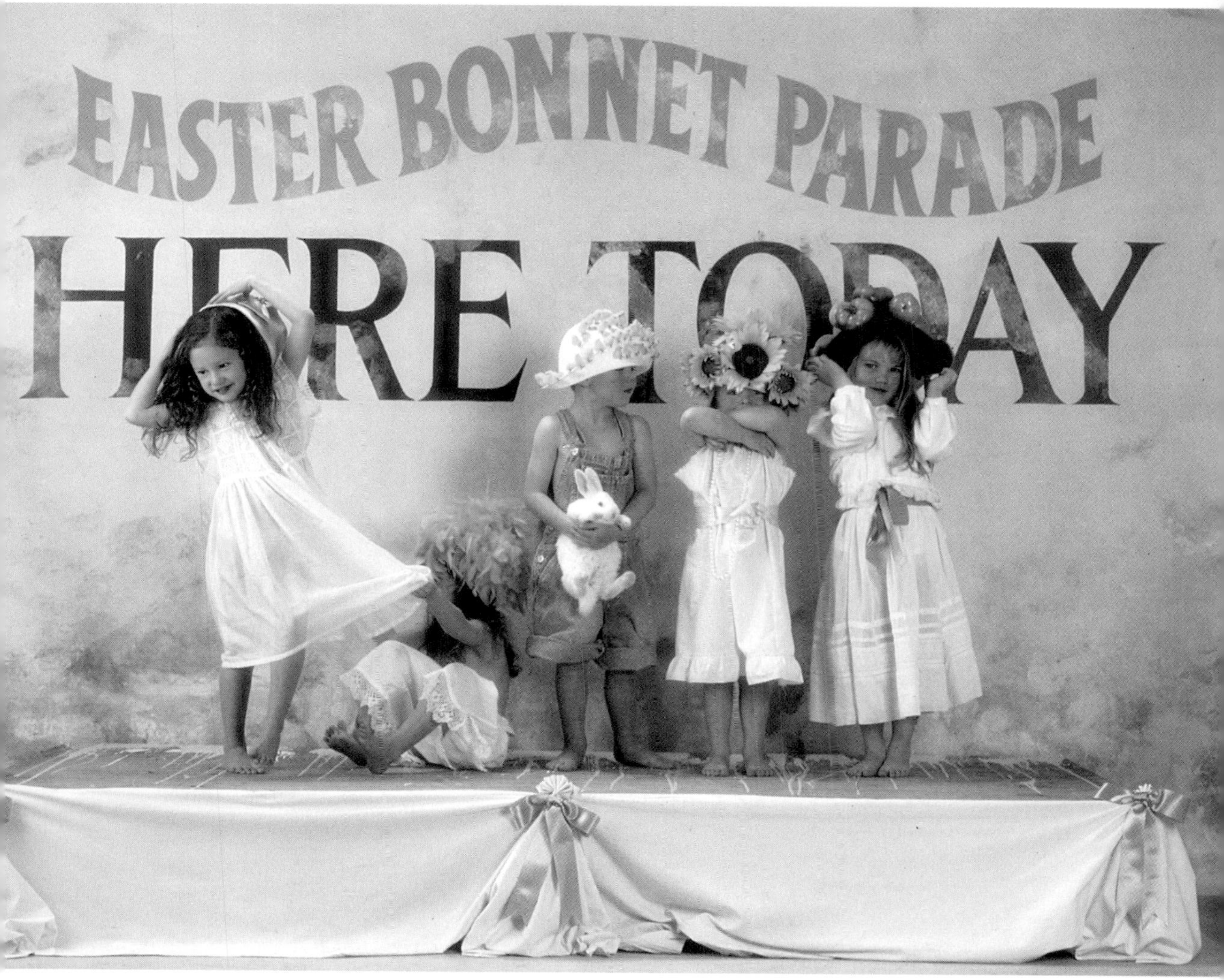
EASTER BONNET PARADE
HERE TODAY

APRIL

SUNDAY
Easter

*Daylight Saving Time
begins in U.S.A.
(Add 1 hour to clock)*

7

MONDAY
*Easter Monday
(Canada)*

8

TUESDAY

9

WEDNESDAY

◑
Last Quarter Moon

10

THURSDAY

11

FRIDAY

12

SATURDAY.

13

APRIL

SUNDAY	14
MONDAY	15
TUESDAY	16
WEDNESDAY	17
● *New Moon*	
THURSDAY	18
FRIDAY	19
SATURDAY	20

APRIL

| SUNDAY | 21 |

| MONDAY | 22 |

| TUESDAY | 23 |

| WEDNESDAY | 24 |

| THURSDAY | 25 |

◐
First Quarter Moon

| FRIDAY | 26 |

| SATURDAY | 27 |

APRIL - MAY

SUNDAY	28
MONDAY	29
TUESDAY	30
WEDNESDAY	1
THURSDAY	2
FRIDAY	3

○
Full Moon

SATURDAY	4

MAY

SUNDAY	5
MONDAY	6
TUESDAY	7
WEDNESDAY	8
THURSDAY	9
FRIDAY	10

◑ *Last Quarter Moon*

SATURDAY	11

ANNE GEDDES

MAY

SUNDAY
Mother's Day

12

MONDAY

13

TUESDAY

14

WEDNESDAY

15

THURSDAY

16

FRIDAY

17

●
New Moon

SATURDAY

18

MAY

SUNDAY	19
MONDAY *Victoria Day* *(Canada)*	20
TUESDAY	21
WEDNESDAY	22
THURSDAY	23
FRIDAY	24
SATURDAY	25

◑ *First Quarter Moon*

ANNE GEDDES

MAY - JUNE

SUNDAY *Pentecost*	26
MONDAY *Memorial Day*	27
TUESDAY	28
WEDNESDAY	29
THURSDAY	30
FRIDAY	31
SATURDAY ○ *Full Moon*	1

ANNE GEDDES

JUNE

SUNDAY	2
MONDAY	3
TUESDAY	4
WEDNESDAY	5
THURSDAY	6
FRIDAY	7
SATURDAY	8

◑
Last Quarter Moon

ANNE GEDDES

JUNE

SUNDAY	9
MONDAY	10
TUESDAY	11
WEDNESDAY	12
THURSDAY	13
FRIDAY *Flag Day*	14
SATURDAY	15

● *New Moon*

ANNE GEDDES

JUNE

SUNDAY
Father's Day

16

MONDAY

17

TUESDAY

18

WEDNESDAY

19

THURSDAY
Summer Solstice
10:25 P.M. E.D.T.

20

FRIDAY

21

SATURDAY

22

JUNE

SUNDAY	23
MONDAY *St. Jean Baptiste Day* *(Quebec)* ◐ *First Quarter Moon*	24
TUESDAY	25
WEDNESDAY	26
THURSDAY	27
FRIDAY	28
SATURDAY	29

ANNE GEDDES

JUNE - JULY

SUNDAY 30

○
Full Moon

MONDAY
Canada Day
1

TUESDAY 2

WEDNESDAY 3

THURSDAY
Independence Day
4

FRIDAY 5

SATURDAY 6

JULY

SUNDAY	7

◑
Last Quarter Moon

MONDAY	8
TUESDAY	9
WEDNESDAY	10
THURSDAY	11
FRIDAY	12
SATURDAY	13

JULY

SUNDAY	14
MONDAY	15

●
New Moon

TUESDAY	16
WEDNESDAY	17
THURSDAY	18
FRIDAY	19
SATURDAY	20

JULY

| SUNDAY | 21 |

| MONDAY | 22 |

| TUESDAY | 23 |

● First Quarter Moon

| WEDNESDAY | 24 |

| THURSDAY | 25 |

| FRIDAY | 26 |

| SATURDAY | 27 |

ANNE GEDDES

JULY - AUGUST

SUNDAY   28

MONDAY   29

TUESDAY   30

○
Full Moon

WEDNESDAY   31

THURSDAY   1

FRIDAY   2

SATURDAY   3

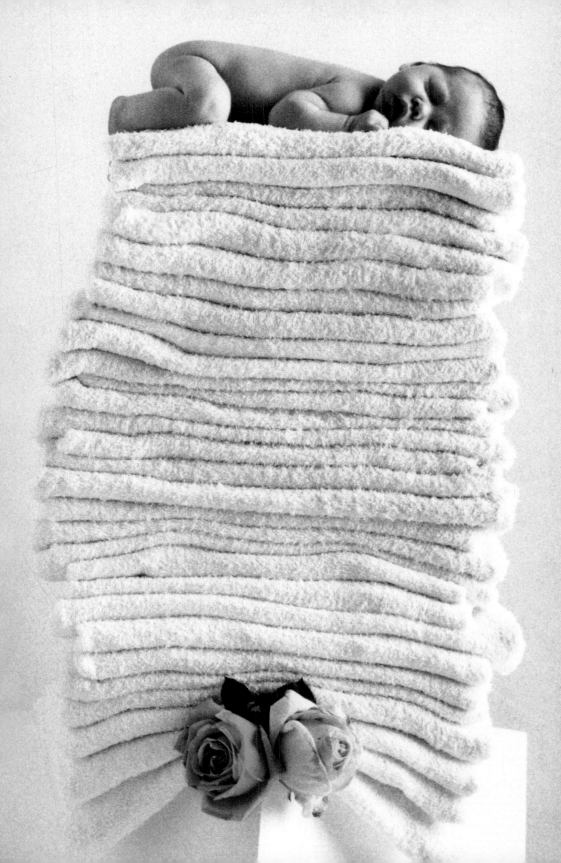

AUGUST

SUNDAY   4

MONDAY   5

TUESDAY   6

◑
Last Quarter Moon

WEDNESDAY   7

THURSDAY   8

FRIDAY   9

SATURDAY   10

AUGUST

SUNDAY   11

MONDAY   12

TUESDAY   13

WEDNESDAY   14

●
New Moon

THURSDAY   15

FRIDAY   16

SATURDAY   17

AUGUST

SUNDAY	18
MONDAY	19
TUESDAY	20
WEDNESDAY	21

◐
First Quarter Moon

THURSDAY	22
FRIDAY	23
SATURDAY	24

AUGUST

SUNDAY	25

MONDAY	26

TUESDAY	27

WEDNESDAY	28

○
Full Moon

THURSDAY	29

FRIDAY	30

SATURDAY	31

SEPTEMBER

SUNDAY   1

MONDAY
Labor Day   2

TUESDAY   3

WEDNESDAY   4

◑
Last Quarter Moon

THURSDAY   5

FRIDAY   6

SATURDAY   7

SEPTEMBER

SUNDAY
Grandparents' Day

8

MONDAY

9

TUESDAY

10

WEDNESDAY

11

THURSDAY

12

●
New Moon

FRIDAY
*Rosh Hashanah
begins (at sunset)*

13

SATURDAY

14

SEPTEMBER

SUNDAY   15

MONDAY   16

TUESDAY   17

WEDNESDAY   18

THURSDAY   19

FRIDAY   20

◐
First Quarter Moon

SATURDAY   21

ANNE GEDDES

SEPTEMBER

SUNDAY	**22**
Yom Kippur begins (at sunset)	
Autumnal Equinox 2:01 P.M. E.D.T.	

MONDAY	**23**

TUESDAY	**24**

WEDNESDAY	**25**

THURSDAY	**26**
○ *Full Moon*	

FRIDAY	**27**

SATURDAY	**28**

SEPTEMBER - OCTOBER

SUNDAY	29
MONDAY	30
TUESDAY	1
WEDNESDAY	2
THURSDAY	3
FRIDAY	4

◑
Last Quarter Moon

SATURDAY	5

OCTOBER

SUNDAY	6
MONDAY	7
TUESDAY	8
WEDNESDAY	9
THURSDAY	10
FRIDAY	11
SATURDAY	12

● *New Moon*

OCTOBER

| SUNDAY | 13 |

| MONDAY
Columbus Day

*Thanksgiving Day
(Canada)* | 14 |

| TUESDAY | 15 |

| WEDNESDAY | 16 |

| THURSDAY | 17 |

| FRIDAY | 18 |

| SATURDAY | 19 |

◑
First Quarter Moon

OCTOBER

SUNDAY	20
MONDAY	21
TUESDAY	22
WEDNESDAY	23
THURSDAY	24
FRIDAY	25
SATURDAY	26

○
Full Moon

OCTOBER - NOVEMBER

SUNDAY
*Daylight Saving Time
ends in U.S.A.
(Subtract 1 hour from clock)*

27

MONDAY

28

TUESDAY

29

WEDNESDAY

30

THURSDAY
Halloween

31

FRIDAY

1

SATURDAY

2

NOVEMBER

SUNDAY	3

◑
Last Quarter Moon

MONDAY	4

TUESDAY	5

Election Day

WEDNESDAY	6

THURSDAY	7

FRIDAY	8

SATURDAY	9

ANNE GEDDES

NOVEMBER

SUNDAY	10

●
New Moon

MONDAY	11

Veterans' Day

Remembrance Day (Canada)

TUESDAY	12

WEDNESDAY	13

THURSDAY	14

FRIDAY	15

SATURDAY	16

NOVEMBER

SUNDAY	17

◑
First Quarter Moon

MONDAY	18
TUESDAY	19
WEDNESDAY	20
THURSDAY	21
FRIDAY	22
SATURDAY	23

NOVEMBER

SUNDAY	24
○ *Full Moon*	
MONDAY	25
TUESDAY	26
WEDNESDAY	27
THURSDAY *Thanksgiving Day*	28
FRIDAY	29
SATURDAY	30

DECEMBER

| SUNDAY | 1 |

| MONDAY | 2 |

| TUESDAY | 3 |

◑
Last Quarter Moon

| WEDNESDAY | 4 |

| THURSDAY | 5 |
Hanukkah begins
(at sunset)

| FRIDAY | 6 |

| SATURDAY | 7 |

DECEMBER

SUNDAY	8
MONDAY	9
TUESDAY	10

● *New Moon*

WEDNESDAY	11
THURSDAY	12
FRIDAY	13
SATURDAY	14

ANNE GEDDES

DECEMBER

SUNDAY	15
MONDAY	16
TUESDAY	17

◐
First Quarter Moon

WEDNESDAY	18
THURSDAY	19
FRIDAY	20
SATURDAY	21

Winter Solstice
9:07 A.M. E.S.T.

DECEMBER

SUNDAY	22
MONDAY	23
TUESDAY	24

○
Full Moon

WEDNESDAY *Christmas Day*	25
THURSDAY *Boxing Day (Canada)*	26
FRIDAY	27
SATURDAY	28

DECEMBER - JANUARY

SUNDAY   29

MONDAY   30

TUESDAY   31

WEDNESDAY   1
New Year's Day

◑
Last Quarter Moon

THURSDAY   2

FRIDAY   3

SATURDAY   4

Notes

Notes